CU00822424

Ben Nevis

and its

Observatory

A Guide to the Ben and to
the Observatory built on
the Summit in 1883

Northern Books
from Famedram

ISBN 0905 489 284

The publishers acknowledge the kind assistance of the West
Highland Museum, Fort William in the preparation of this guide.

© Copyright 1983-2004 Famedram Publishers Ltd.
www.northernbooks.co.uk

Printed by Thomson Press (I), C-35 Phase II, Noida

Introduction

ON OCTOBER 17th 1883 a bizarre ceremony on the summit of Ben Nevis marked the opening of an extraordinary era in the history of the mountain. An observatory was founded right on the summit and for the next 20 years it was home winter and summer, night and day to a team of meteorological observers who, come storm, tempest or hurricane, made hourly recordings of climatic conditions at the top of the mountain.

For those who carried out this often perilous undertaking conditions were often appalling. The winds could be so strong that two men roped together and crawling across the snow were in danger of being blown away to their certain death down one of the precipices that abound on the summit of Britain's highest mountain.

The first observatory on Ben Nevis had actually been 'constructed' a couple of years earlier, in 1881. A Mr Clement L. Wragge had offered to undertake what was effectively a feasibility study for the project by climbing to the top of the mountain every day throughout the summer and making observations on the top. To assist him in this task he built a rude stone shelter covered with a tarpaulin.

The results of this tireless application were so encouraging that the following year, in 1882, he had the help of his wife and two assistants and a whole series of readings was made at various levels. The results obtained from this work led the Scottish Meterological Society to launch an appeal, early in 1883, for funds to build a permanent observatory on the summit. The response was incredible. In no time at all nearly £5,000 was subscribed. 'Her Most Gracious Majesty' Queen Victoria sent £50, as did the Duke of Argyll. The Dukes of Buccleuch and Devonshire managed £100 each, while a James Young of Kelly stumped up £200. Numerous smaller donations are recorded, including one of three guineas from a 'Robert Younger', St Ann's Brewery, Edinburgh and £10 from the magistrates and council of Inverness.

Work started immediately and during the summer of 1883 a bridle path was constructed right to the summit (for a cost of some £800) and materials were carried up.

The initial building was a relatively simple affair and through the first winter of 1883-4 – an appallingly harsh one – its shortcomings became only too obvious.

The superintendent of the observatory, a Mr R.T. Ormond, reported: "As no arrangement had been made for keeping the doorway of the observatory clear of snowdrift, during bad weather almost constant digging was required...On several occasions during the night watches the drift came in faster than

one man could shovel it out, and there was nothing
for it but to bar the door and wait till morning, when
all hands could be employed to re-open communication with the outside world...When the snow
reached its full winter depth of ten or twelve feet, all
attempts to keep this doorway clear were hopeless.''

The solution was to enlarge the observatory and to
alter the layout so that the instruments on the tower
could be reached from a high level door that was not
liable to become blocked by snow.

In the summer of 1884 several extra rooms were
added, built, interestingly, by a method similar to
the timber frame 'kit' method used for many of
today's dream houses on private estates. The difference, of course, being in the thickness of stone
wall surrounding the timber frame. At their base the
stone walls used for the observatory buildings were
as much as twelve feet thick.

The new designs proved highly successful and Mr
Omond was able to report that through the following winter the schedule of hourly readings night and
day was faithfully adhered to, with only one serious
interruption on the night of February 21, 1885
when, for 15 hours on end it was impossible to make
any readings, even with two observers roped together.

Provisioning of the observatory took place during
the summer months, when supplies and fuel suf-
ficient for up to nine months, were ferried up to the
summit on a pony train. In the winter the observers
kept in touch with the outside world via a telegraph
cable. There was also a grandly named Observatory
Road Surveyor who trekked up to the summit with a

supply of letters and newspapers every two or three weeks, when conditions permitted.

The building of the observatory attracted enormous attention in Victorian Britain and in the summer visitors climbed the mountain in their thousands. For the use of the track to the summit foot passengers were charged one shilling, while those on horseback were asked to pay three shillings. Permits were to be had "either from the booksellers in Fort William, or from the caretaker of the road, by whom they will be dated and stamped."

The level of interest led eventually to the opening of an 'hotel' on the summit. In fact the establishment opened by a Mr White of Fort William was little more than a large wooden shed but, assisted by a team of young ladies from the town, he was able to offer refreshment and simple accommodation to those who had found the pilgrimage too taxing.

Observations were kept up for some 21 years, but even in those far-off times the public purse was not a bottomless one and by 1904 the directors of the observatory were finding it impossible to match income to expenditure. Overall running costs were put at some £1000 a year, (a figure which included the costs of maintaining the low level station in Fort William). An annual grant of £350 came from the Meteorological Council, the balance being found by the directors from a variety of sources.

After questions in Parliament on the subejct a Treasury Committee was appointed to look into the whole question of the funding of the Meteorological Council. Inevitably this led to consideration of the value of the work done on Ben Nevis. Opinions

Introduction

differed. Lord Kelvin told the committee of enquiry that he thought the observations "of the highest utility," while a Professor Schuster felt that "the problems that could with convenience be carried out have been dealt with."

In the event the Treasury committee recommended continuance of the £350 grant. But since this left the directors of the observatory with the task of raising some £650 annually they decided to give up the struggle and on October 1, 1904 the hourly observations were discontinued. A week later, on October 8, just a week short of its twenty first birthday, the observatory door was barricaded and locked up for the last time.

The account that follows was prepared by the directors and first published in the summer of 1893. At that time the future of the observatory seemed assured. Many of the photographs accompanying the text are taken from *Twenty Years on Ben Nevis* by William T. Kilgour. The two sketches are from an earlier guide to the observatory and were executed by Messrs George Reid and Archibald Geikie.

Ben Nevis and its Observatory

———•———

ASCENT OF BEN NEVIS.

BEN NEVIS is usually climbed from Fort-William or Banavie, the ascent taking three to four hours from either place. From the former the route is to follow the high road from the north end of the town as far as Nevis Bridge—about ten minutes' walk—then cross the bridge, and immediately after turn off into a side road to the right. Care must be taken not to follow a similar road that leaves the main road just before the bridge —it leads up Glen Nevis, but at the other side of the river from the mountain. Persons starting from Banavie and following the road to Fort-William, reach Nevis Bridge from the other direction, and of course turn to the *left before* crossing the bridge. Continuing along the side road for a mile and a half, the farm of Achintee is reached, where the Observatory bridle-path will be seen sloping upwards to the left. From this point to the summit of the Ben the distance by the path is almost exactly five miles, and as in this comparatively short distance a rise of over 4000 feet has to be made, the gradient is necessarily somewhat steep.

Ascent of Ben Nevis

At first the track slants upwards along the side of Glen Nevis, crossing some small streams on wooden bridges, and, after a little, rising by two sharp turns into more rocky ground ; shortly after the second of these turns, a longer wooden bridge over a steep narrow gorge is crossed, and the climber may congratulate himself on having accomplished fully one quarter of the ascent, the elevation of this bridge being about 1200 feet above sea-level. All along this first part the view is mainly restricted to Glen Nevis and the hills that surround it.[1]

The road now turns to the left, and enters the short side valley of Coire na h-Urchairean. This is often the most trying part of the ascent ; the valley is usually close and airless, and the stranger ascending for the first time finds it almost as difficult to reach the top of the corrie as to pronounce its name, but when the former is accomplished he finds himself on a comparatively level piece of road, with the view to the north up the Caledonian Canal valley opening before him. The road now passes above a small lake, and then turns back to a little hut, at or near which visitors are usually asked to pay for the use of the road. This hut, which affords a welcome shelter in bad weather, is

[1] The lower three-fourths of Ben Nevis are composed of a coarsely crystalline pink granite, becoming finer grained towards the top, traversed by abundant veins of pale fine-grained granite and eurite, and of dark porphyry and diabase. The upper fourth of the mountain consists of a dark porphyry which often shows on weathered faces a remarkable brecciated character and streaky fluxion-structure, which are not traceable on a fresh fracture. The silurian crystalline schists through which the granite rises are well seen where the road to the mountain leaves the highway.

2200 feet above the sea, or just half the height of the mountain. When descending the hill it is possible to take a short cut from near the hut straight down to the road below, but this should not be tried going up, as the ground is boggy and slippery, making the gain of time infinitesimal and the extra expenditure of strength considerable. Many visitors from Banavie take the old track up the north side of the hill, and join the Observatory road at this point: on this latter route a guide is advisable for strangers, as there is no distinct path in many places.

After leaving the hut, the road crosses, by the last of the wooden bridges, the Red Burn, just below a small waterfall, and thereafter ascends the western shoulder of Ben Nevis in six long zigzags, each of which opens a wider and more varied view as the climber gradually rises above the lower heights round. Near the top of the fifth of these turns a spring of water is passed coming out of a rock on the left side of the road: this is the last water on the road below the summit, and marks the accomplishment of three-fourths of the ascent. Above this well the hill consists almost wholly of bare rock, splintered and broken up by the frost, and showing scarcely a trace of vegetation: but the road, though rough and stony, soon relapses to an easier gradient, and winds across an irregular plateau for about half a mile. In sheltered hollows on this plateau snow often lies long into the summer; patches may be seen here even in July or August, when the summit of the hill is quite bare. One short steep ascent only remains,

known as ' Maclean's Steep,' up which the road runs in
three sharp turns; but if the day be clear, the visitor is
cheered and encouraged by seeing that he is over-
topping all the hills in the neighbourhood, and once
the steep part is left behind, five minutes' walk along a
comparatively level broad-topped ridge brings him to
the highest point. The northern or left-hand side of
this ridge is a continuous precipice, 1500 to 2000 feet
deep, which, if the visitor leaves the beaten track, should
be approached with caution, care being especially
taken not to step on any of the snow-wreaths that in
early summer often fringe its edge, and may give way
at any moment.

The first building seen on the top is the refreshment
rooms, called 'Observatory Hotel' by its proprietor;
a short distance behind may be seen the dark stone
walls and tower of the Observatory. The latter stands
within a few yards of the Ordnance cairn that marks
the highest point.

The view from the summit on a clear day is one of
the most extensive in Scotland. To the northward,
looking across the deep gorges and side spurs of Ben
Nevis, we see a comparatively level plain extending
from Fort-William to the entrance of Glen Spean, up
which glen, to the N.E., a glimpse may be had of Loch
Laggan and the opening through which the road passes
to Kingussie, with, in the background, the massive
ridge of the Cairngorms, among which Ben Macdhui,
the second highest hill in Britain, can be with difficulty
distinguished. The northern side of Glen Spean is

The observatory perched above a sheer drop.

High summer atop the Ben.

formed by the rounded masses of the Monagh Lea hills, running up into which Glen Roy with its 'Parallel Roads' may be noticed; and due north from Ben Nevis lies the end of Loch Lochy, the first lake on the Caledonian Canal. In very clear weather some of the buildings of Inverness and the high ground of the Black Isle beyond can be seen, while the rounded outline of Ben Wyvis distinguishes it from the sharper summits of the Ross-shire hills to the N.W. Passing over the wilderness of hills in northern Inverness-shire, among which Mam Soul and Scour-Ouran (Loch Hourn) are the most prominent, the jagged outlines of the Coolins in Skye may be easily distinguished rising above the lower heights between. Looking over the head of Locheil, the islands of Rum and Eigg form a magnificent background to the rather tame slopes of the mainland; and in the clear space of sea between Rum and Skye a few heights of the Outer Hebrides may sometimes be discerned, but their distance is about ninety miles, and it needs exceptionally clear weather to bring them into view.

Looking southward, the dark ridges of the Glencoe hills overtop the nearer heights on the other side of Glen Nevis. Beyond them the horizon is closed by the long ridge of Ben Cruachan, and the tumbled masses of hills to the eastward of it. To the right of all these, Loch Linnhe stretches away down to the open sea, bounded on the farther side by the hills of Morven and Mull, and opening the view to the distant islands: Lismore in Loch Linnhe itself, Jura with two conical hills, Islay almost hid behind Jura, Colonsay half hid behind Mull, and the many craggy islets that dot the sea between. On exceptionally clear days, when the horizon is free from all haze, the high ground of N.E. Ireland is seen as a dark line crossing the sea between Jura and the mainland. South-eastward from Ben Nevis the desolate plateau of the Moor of Rannoch extends to the borders of Perthshire. Beyond it the most prominent hills are the double peak of Ben More and Stobinian, the elevated ridge of Ben Vorlich (near Comrie), the rather shapeless heights of Ben Lawers and its neighbours, and, standing alone, the sharp cone of Schiehallion.

It is seldom that all these hills can be seen at one time ; clouds may obscure the view in one direction while in another it may be quite clear, and not infrequently a cloud-cap on Ben Nevis itself circumscribes the whole view to a few yards. Sometimes the cloud layer of the atmosphere is all below, then the sun shines down from a cloudless sky, while the lower world is concealed under a level-topped sheet of fleecy cloud, through which the higher hill-tops project like islands in a sea. It is then that, if the spectator can stand so that his shadow is thrown on to the fog below, Brocken Spectres and Glories may be observed : they are of course most frequently seen near sunrise or sunset, when the shadow is projected to a greater distance, and are most curious and interesting when rising swirls of fog approach the summit. The best place for seeing these phenomena, and a point worth going to for its own sake, is the eastern extremity of the hill-top. Leaving the highest point, a few minutes' scramble along the rough boulders of the top brings the visitor to a projecting point surrounded on three sides by precipices, from which he can look down into the great corries of the northern cliff.

The ascent of Ben Nevis in winter, when the greater part of the hill is covered with deep snow, is a more serious undertaking. A fine day is absolutely necessary and an experienced guide desirable. For several months it is scarcely possible to follow the road farther than the half-way hut, as it is often lost in snow. The usual route is to go from the hut directly up the hill at the back of it, a very steep and rough climb, but a route on which the snow does not usually lie very deep. Once up this hill, the track over the summit is indicated by guide-posts, which mark out a safe route to the Observatory. The fatigue of the climb depends on the quality of the snow more than on its depth. If the snow is freshly fallen and soft the ascent is almost impossible, but when compacted by alternate thaw and frost it becomes hard as a rock and can be walked on with comparative ease. Few strangers attempt the climb in winter, but the Observatory Road Overseer makes frequent ascents with letters and newspapers, and takes down the records of the observations. In moderate weather he may go up at intervals of a week or ten days, but when heavy falls of snow and strong winds have prevailed the observers have on rare occasions been five or six weeks without seeing him.

LIFE AND WORK ON BEN NEVIS.

The object aimed at in a Meteorological Observatory of the First Class is to get a continuous record of the elements which control and constitute the weather. At most of such stations, including the Fort-William Observatory, this is done by self-recording instruments, which trace out on a moving sheet of paper the barometric pressure, temperature, wind, rainfall, etc., continuously, in conjunction with which it is only necessary to take a few eye-readings each day as a check and control on the instruments. But on the summit of Ben Nevis the clock-work and other delicate mechanism of the instruments would be unworkable. No such apparatus has yet been devised capable of registering correctly in the free atmosphere when exposed to long continued gales laden with frozen fog and snow-drift. In order to get a practically continuous register on Ben Nevis recourse had therefore to be had to hourly eye-readings of the various instruments. This necessitates two observers, who keep watch alternately both by day and by night.

During the first winter (1883-1884) only part of the Observatory was built, and it was found impossible to carry out this scheme completely. No arrangement having been made for keeping the doorway of the Observatory clear of snow-drift during bad weather, almost constant digging was required ; while before there were more than two or three feet of snow lying on the open

17

hill-top, great drifts had accumulated round the house, rising almost to the roof, and completely hiding the walls. A passage had to be dug outwards and upwards through this, which though quite easily kept clear in fine weather, was constantly filled up as soon as the wind rose, bringing with it whirling snowdrift up the sides of the hill and over the buildings. This difficulty was partly overcome by constructing an archway of blocks of snow and tarpaulins over the snow steps leading up from the door, but as no door could be placed at the upper end of this arch-way or tunnel, there was always the danger of drift blowing down into it, and choking it. On several occasions during the night-watches the drift came in faster than one man could shovel it out; and there was nothing for it but to bar the door, and wait till morning, when all hands could be employed to re-open com-munication with the outside world by an hour or two of spade drill—good exercise, no doubt, but a kind of work not usually included in the routine of an Observatory. When the snow reached its full winter depth of ten or twelve feet, all attempts to keep this doorway clear in bad weather were hopeless. Even as late as the beginning of May 1884 the continuity of the outside observations was broken from this cause. In the summer of that year, however, large additions were made to the Observatory buildings (see page 35), in which arrangements were made for exit in all weathers.

With all these difficulties to be encountered, the observations during the first winter were necessarily somewhat incomplete. Independently of observations

The squat stone walls of the observatory.

Building work in progress.

lost by stress of weather, there was every night, that is, some time between 9 P.M. and 9 A.M., a watch of four hours in which no outside observations were taken. Since May 1884, however, the observations have comprised a complete set of readings of all the instruments, outside as well as inside the Observatory, at every hour, by night as well as by day.

The day of twenty-four hours is divided into watches, —eight hours at night and four during the day. Thus there is always at least one of the observers keeping watch over the weather, and going out punctually at each hour to read the various instruments and make notes. The actual observation takes only from five to ten minutes, but during the remainder of the time there is plenty to do in reducing and filling up the daily records, checking the results, and drawing up daily and monthly averages of the readings of each instrument.[1] Since May 1884 this regular routine has only once or twice been interrupted. On the night of the 21st of February 1885 a terrific southerly gale blew with hurricane force, and stopped all outside observing for fifteen hours. It was impossible to stand or even to crawl to windward, while the most carefully-shielded lantern was blown out at once. During the height of the gale the air was full of snow-drift, intermixed with which were

[1] The instruments in regular use comprise a Fortin Barometer; Thermometers, Dry and Wet Bulbs, Maximum and Minimum, Radiation (Black Bulb *in vacuo*); Rain or Snow Gauge of special design; Ozone Tests; Campbell's Sunshine Recorder; Anemometers for Direction and Velocity of the Wind; Photographic Apparatus; and Dust-Counting Apparatus.

great lumps of hardened snow that had been torn from the ground by the violence of the wind. One of these flying pieces broke the only window that was above the snow and exposed to the gale, and another smashed half-a-dozen louvres in the Stevenson's screen for the thermometers. This gale was the severest experienced in any winter. Occasionally similar conditions of wind and overpowering drift have occurred, but only for an hour or two at a time, and long-continued gales have not been accompanied by so much drift. During the months of February and March it is not uncommon to have south-easterly gales blowing for three or four days continuously, at the rate of eighty to a hundred miles an hour; but under these circumstances the hill-top is usually swept at once clear of all loose snow, and a hard surface of rough ice left, which is not touched by the wind, and on which good footing may be got. At first, when the surface was icy and the wind very strong, the observers used to go out roped together, but experience has shown that even in the most violent gusts safety may be always got by lying down, and the rope is seldom used except when it is necessary to go to very exposed places. For the ordinary observations a guide-line for use at night in case of the lantern being blown out is all that is required. In steady winds the angle at which the observer leans in order to keep his footing becomes a valuable factor in estimating the wind-force. The storms of early winter—November and December—usually bring a thaw and heavy rain, which though very disagreeable does not interrupt the usual course of observing ; the most unpleasant weather is when it rains while the temperature is still below freezing. The rain then freezes as it falls and everything gets covered with hard ice, which may increase in thickness indefinitely, the only limit being the time that these conditions continue. On one occasion it lasted for two days, and the ice was more than a foot thick both on the ground and on the windward side of all projections. This deposit of ice or snow on all exposed surfaces is one of the chief difficulties connected with the working of the instruments of the Observatory : it occurs whenever there is fog or mist on the summit.

During summer, or when the temperature is above the freezing-point, the fog soaks everything exposed to it. All the instruments outside, and indeed all exposed surfaces, stream with moisture, even though there may be no rain actually falling. In winter, when the temperature is below freezing, the effect of the fog is to cover everything with long feathery masses of crystalline snow. It seems that as the fog is driven across the hilltop by the wind, and brushes against any obstruction, the moisture in it condenses in minute crystalline specks of snow or hoar-frost ; these accumulate until long cone-shaped crystals are formed pointing to windward, which grow by continual accretion till they break off by their own weight. These crystals sometimes grow till they form a solid massive pillar about three feet in diameter, the nucleus of the whole being a simple wooden post, some six inches by three in section. This is usually the result of several days' growth, during which time the wind

Inside the observatory.

shifts so as to deposit crystals from all sides on the post ; but even when care is taken to keep the exposed object as clear as possible, it is impossible to wholly prevent their formation. During dense fog they will often grow at the rate of fully two feet a day. Any attempt to preserve the insulation of electrical instruments exposed to such conditions is obviously hopeless, and the many ingenious self-recording meteorological instruments used at lower levels, or under more favourable conditions, are useless. Specially devised anemometers for registering the direction, pressure, and velocity of the wind have been placed on the tower of the Observatory. During summer they work well, but in winter they are virtually useless owing to this accretion upon them of snow crystals from the fog. This growth rapidly chokes the louvres of the thermometer screen ; if the temperature is low the crystals are loose and easily brushed off; but if near the freezing-point, even without the objectionable rain mentioned above, the crystals are hard and icy, and adhere firmly, needing to be chipped off. This difficulty with the thermometer screen has been overcome by using duplicate screens. When the one in use gets badly choked, no attempt is made to clear it, but it is taken in bodily and a fresh screen with other thermometers inside is put out. The screens are placed, in wintertime, on a high stand shaped like a ladder so that the instruments can be put stage by stage higher up as the snow gets deeper, and may always be about four feet above the surface of the snow. In summer when the top is clear of snow an ordinary Stevenson screen is used. In these screens are four thermometers—dry bulb, wet bulb, maximum and minimum. The dry and wet are read hourly, the maximum and minimum once a day at nine p.m. Thus a practically continuous record is got of the shade temperature from the dry bulb and of the humidity and water vapour present in the air from the wet bulb, while the range, or highest and lowest temperatures, are checked by the maximum and minimum. These are shade temperatures; in summer and in fine weather in winter sun temperatures are also taken with black bulb *in vacuo* thermometers, but these instruments are useless in snowstorms and frozen fogs.

There has been recently added another form of thermometer screen, for use in weather when it might be dangerous to go out. An opening made in the wall (*A*) of the tower about eighteen feet above the ground is fitted with a stout door (*B*) opening inwards (see diagram) ; on the outer side of this door a louvred screen (*S*) is hung on pintles and secured with a cord : through a socket in the door a long bent thermometer is passed, mounted in a brass frame that fits the socket tightly ; the part above the bend has the scale (*T*) which is read inside the tower, while the bulb end (*t*) is outside in the louvred screen. A small trap door (*b*) enables one to examine the inside of the screen, which has no louvres on the side next the tower. Experience has shown that during strong winds this thermometer, especially at night, reads almost identically with that in the Stevenson screen. The difference after correction for instrumental errors never exceeds three- or four-

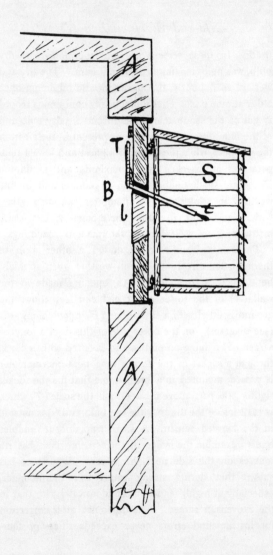

tenths of a degree, and on the average of a night's readings is usually only one-tenth. During calm weather or strong sunshine, the readings are not reliable, the thermometer being too near the warm wall of the tower, but under such circumstances they are not required. Duplicate screens are used in the same way as with the Stevenson, but it is seldom necessary to change them during the course of a storm ; with a wind of, say, eighty miles an hour searching into every cranny, ventilation may be reduced to a minimum without affecting the accuracy of the thermometric readings.

The use of this tower thermometer considerably diminishes the excitement of life at the Observatory. Formerly, the observer, after equipping himself in oil-skins from head to foot like a North Sea pilot, struggled through wind and drift to the thermometers ; but now a brief exposure to the storm to estimate the wind is all that is necessary, the barometer and thermometer are read under shelter, and the rain or snow gauges are useless in such a storm. The slight probable error in temperature introduced by using the tower screen in such a storm is more than balanced by the greater certainty and accuracy with which the thermometers can be read ; on the outside thermometers tenths of degrees become doubtful when the observer's eyes have first to be cleared of snow-drift and then the stems of the thermometers wiped before reading. Another time at which this sheltered thermometer may be used is in thunderstorms. Fortunately thunder-storms are rare on Ben Nevis ; on the average there are only about half a dozen in the year, mostly in autumn and winter; and there have been intervals of as long as two years without either thunder or lightning being observed. Most of the ordinary summer thunderstorms seem to pass below the hill-top, and even the thunder is not heard. But when a storm does pass over the summit, it is a most unpleasant experience. The cloud is seen approaching with lightning flashing from it; it then envelops the hill-top, during which time no lightning is seen, but rain or snow falls heavily —as much as one-third of an inch in ten minutes has been recorded: and then, as the cloud moves off, a discharge takes place, not merely from the cloud, but from all large metallic bodies in the Observatory; a brilliant flash springs out from the stoves, and a sharp crack like a pistol-shot is heard. Some of the observers have received shocks under these circumstances, but no serious harm has been inflicted. The most severe of these storms was in January 1890; one of the observers was almost knocked down when sitting writing, and the telegraph-wire was fused, and all communication stopped for five days. This is the only occasion in eight years that the telegraph-wire has failed,—a very different record from that of High-Level Observatories situated in regions where summer thunderstorms are felt at greater heights.

Another electrical phenomenon sometimes seen is the continuous discharge from elevated points known as St. Elmo's Fire. It usually appears like little jets of flame on the lightning-rod, anemometers, etc., but in the

Snow and fog crystals on the tower.

more brilliant displays every post and chimney is tipped with fire, and sparks glimmer on the observer's hat, pencil, or fingers. It is always accompanied by a peculiar hissing or buzzing noise, and almost invariably by a heavy fall of soft hail or conical-shaped snow. Most frequent in winter, it may sometimes be observed in stormy weather in summer. One July evening, the observer, on going out at nine p.m., had his attention first drawn to a high post which was sounding like a telegraph-pole carrying a 'noisy wire,' and on turning his face up to the sky he felt a gentle pricking sensation all over it. The daylight was too bright to see anything, but the noise lasted for a quarter of an hour or more. St. Elmo's Fire occurs in weather of the type that accompanies thunderstorms in the British Isles.

The optical meteorological phenomena observed on Ben Nevis are of great interest and beauty. As the observers are practically in the clouds for most of the time, many opportunities are afforded of minutely examining the optical effects of mist or cloud on the rays of the sun or moon. The most interesting sights of this class are seen during moderately fine winter weather, when the hill-top is clear of all dense fog, but the atmosphere not too dry. When a thin, almost imperceptible, film of scud-cloud or mist covers the moon, coronæ of the most vivid colours are formed. These coronæ, as is well known, consist of coloured rings arranged concentrically round the moon or sun. Each ring has all the usual spectroscopic or rainbow colours to more or less perfection arranged with the red belt outside. A very curious and not uncommon type is one in which there is a well-marked red ring with yellow and blue inside, but with also a blue margin or glare outside it. The colours inside and including the red make up the usual spectrum, and this margin is a kind of extra and unbalanced development of blue. Professor Tait has supplied the Observatory with an instrument devised specially for the measurement of the angular size of these and similar objects, and already some valuable results, bearing on questions of diffraction and the size of water particles, have been obtained from it.

Another allied optical phenomenon is what are called Glories. In winter when the sun is low, even at noon, the shadow of a person standing near the cliff that runs all along the northern side of Ben Nevis is cast clear of the hill into the valley below. In bright winter weather this deep gloomy gorge is often full of loose shifting fog, and when the shadow falls upon it, the observer sees his head surrounded by a series of coloured rings, from two to five in number, varying in size from a mere blotch of light up to a well-defined arch six or eight degrees in radius. This phenomenon does not present quite the same appearance as the better known Brocken Spectre, for here the shadow of the observer, in consequence of the distance of the mist from him, does not appear unnaturally large ; in fact the image of the head appears as a mere dark speck in the centre of the coloured rings. These glories are less common in summer, though they have been seen near sunrise and sunset. The sun is too high at noon to cast the shadow far enough, and the atmospheric conditions are not so favourable to the formation of the necessary fog in the valleys. The exaggerated size may be sometimes noticed when, near sunset, the shadow is thrown on very thin fog; it then forms a long dark tunnel running back into the fog, and appears further away than it really is, the necessary condition for apparent enlargement.

Rainbows are seldom seen from the Ben. During the showery weather required for their formation, the summit of the hill is usually shrouded in mist, and the view limited to some twenty yards. Fog-bows, however, are often seen, both solar and lunar, being formed on the loose fog driving across and around the hill when the top is clearing after a misty day. They frequently accompany Glories, but are quite distinct from them. The laws governing the arrangement of colours in them and in the Glories is not yet quite understood; in Glories the red side of the Spectrum is always outside, in Fog-bows it may form either the outer or inner edge of the arch.

Several Halos of interest have been observed. The ordinary circles of 22° and 45° radius are often seen, and on one occasion a part of the rare arc of about 90° was observed. This is believed to be the fourth instance on record of this unusually large halo. Contact arches touching the ordinary halos, and Mock Suns, either white or coloured, have also been observed, and, not infrequently, the vertical pillar passing up or down from the sun's disc; once this latter form was noticed

A pony train on the bridle path.

Readings were taken at the half-way station.

passing down between the Observatory and the hills at the other side of Glen Nevis, showing that the snow crystals forming it were less than three miles distant, and were floating below the level of Ben Nevis. Copies of the measurements of Coronæ, Halos, Glories, and Fog-bows, and detailed descriptions of them, will be found in the Proceedings of the Royal Society of Edinburgh.

Many of the most interesting views are obtained at sunrise, though the visitor who spends the night on the summit, and sallies forth in the morning enveloped in all the wraps he can lay his hands on, too often finds nothing but mist to reward him. But on a fine summer morning, when the Earth's shadow creeps slowly down the western sky as the Sun comes up behind the Cairngorm mountains, the strange beauty of the scene cannot be easily surpassed. All the valleys beneath have a cold grey look, often interspaced with streaks of fog along the water-courses, and after the sun is fairly up, the shadow of Ben Nevis appears as a great cone on the south-western horizon. The morning hours are not the time at which the hill-top has most chance of being clear, as many believe. It has been found that in the afternoon (1 to 5 p.m.) there are fewest foggy hours, and in the early morning (1 to 6 a.m.) most; but the proportion is only about five to six, and practically when the top is clear it remains clear all day long. The clearest month is June, with about half its days clear, and the foggiest months are November and January, with only one day in four clear.

Animal life, though scarce, is not altogether absent even in winter. Snow buntings build their nests among the rocks of the northern cliff and flit about on the top. Hawks and ravens too are frequently seen, but other birds are only occasional visitors. There are usually a pair or more of stoats somewhere about the summit; they seem to hunt all over the hill, and when hard pressed for food have been known to invade the store-room of the Observatory. Footmarks of hares and foxes may often be seen in the snow, and the red deer occasionally come up to within a few hundred feet of the summit. In summer-time butterflies and other insects have been noticed, and many flies are found lying frozen on the snow in fine weather at all seasons.

ORIGIN AND HISTORY OF THE OBSERVATORY.

The objects of the Science of Meteorology are to discover general principles connected with the state of the atmosphere in reference to temperature, pressure, humidity, and motion, both vertically and horizontally, in different places at different periods of the year; and to apply this knowledge for the purpose of forecasting weather. For each of these objects it is necessary that we should have observations of the conditions of the atmosphere as extensive and as widely spread as possible, both in time and place. We can vary the *time* of observation at will, and can indeed make the observations continuous; but we are much more restricted in our choice of *place*. Practically we are confined to stations on the earth's surface; for although valuable information may be obtained by noting the forms and movements of clouds, and the spectroscopic character of the light from various parts of the sky, and in certain cases by the use of captive balloons, we have no means of continuously comparing the state of the upper atmosphere with that which is under observation at lower Meteorological Stations. Yet the fact that the weather-wise derive their hints almost entirely from the face of the sky, shows the importance of even such imperfect indications as can be thus gained of what is going on above.

It was recognised that the only way in which we could hope to learn something more certain as to the vertical variation of the atmospheric conditions, was to make regular observations at stations as near one another as possible on the map, and differing as much as possible in elevation. The late Mr. Thomas Stevenson, in 1875, proposed, in order to obtain such vertical meteorological sections of the atmosphere for pressure, temperature, humidity, etc., to establish stations at the bottom and top of some steep mountain, and if possible at intermediate heights. In the meantime High-Level Meteorological Observations began to be established in the United States, Mexico, India, and the Australian Colonies : and on the Continent of Europe, in France, Italy, Switzerland, Austria, Bavaria, Russia, and Germany. But for some time in this general movement Great Britain took no part, the highest Meteorological Station being the Society's Station at Dalnaspidal, which is only 1414 feet above the sea.

In 1877 Mr. Milne Home, then Chairman of the Council of the Scottish Meteorological Society, pointed out the singular advantages of Ben Nevis as a High-Level Station. It is the highest mountain in the British Islands (4406 feet) ; its summit is, in horizontal distance, about four miles from a Sea-Level Station at Fort-William, and is situated in the track of the south-west storms from the Atlantic, which exercise such a preponderating influence on the weather of Europe, especially in autumn and winter. Its advantages are therefore unique, and observations made there have proved to be of the greatest interest and value to Meteorology.

The Scottish Meteorological Society accordingly resolved to erect a permanent observatory on the top, and a plan was prepared by Mr. Stevenson in 1879, and offers were received from contractors, but nothing could be done at that time for want of the necessary funds.

In the end of 1880 Mr. Clement L. Wragge wrote to the Society, offering to ascend the mountain daily during the next summer, and make observations at the summit simultaneously with observations made at Fort-William—the Society defraying the expense connected with the work. This offer was accepted, and from June to October 1881 simultaneous observations were made, without a break of a single day, by Mr. Wragge at the top and by Mrs. Wragge at Fort-William. A second series of observations on a much more extended scale was made by Mr. Wragge and two assistants during the summer of 1882, from June to November. A number of stations, extending from Fort-William to the top of Ben Nevis, were established at different heights on the side of the mountain. Readings were made at these stations both on the outward and on the homeward journeys : and, simultaneously with these, complete observations with all the instruments were made at Fort-William, amounting to twenty-one daily. This elaborate system of observations was carried out by Mr. Wragge with a skill, energy, resolution, and success, worthy of all praise. The instruments were provided by the Society, and the expenses, amounting for the two years to £450, were defrayed by special funds at the disposal of the Society, and by the following grants :—£200 from the Meteorological Council, London ; £100 from the Royal Society of Edinburgh ; and £50 from the British Association ; while £50 was obtained from the Government Research Fund to aid in reducing the observations of 1881. During the summer of 1883 similar observations were carried on by Messrs. Rankin and Whyte, who had formerly acted as assistants to Mr. Wragge.

Dr. Buchan's discussions of Mr. Wragge's observations brought out results of the greatest interest. A certain distribution of pressure, temperature, and humidity, being adopted provisionally as the normal condition of the atmosphere, deviations from the normal were noted from time to time, and compared with subsequent changes of weather. From these comparisons conclusive evidence was obtained of the justice of the high expectations which had been formed regarding the part

An intrepid observer breaking ice off the anemometer.

"Wiring the daily report, 9.15 pm, May 3, 1885."

to be played by a High-Level Station on Ben Nevis in forecasting the weather of the British Islands.

Sensible of the great importance of a High-Level Meteorological Station for Great Britain, the Council of the Scottish Meteorological Society, strengthened by Representatives of the Royal Society of London, the Royal Society of Edinburgh, and the Glasgow Philosophical Society, who form the Board of Directors, made an appeal to the public, in the early part of 1883, for funds to enable them to build an Observatory on the summit of Ben Nevis.

The greatest interest was manifested in the proposal by scientific men both at home and abroad, and the Meteorological Council of London offered £100 annually towards the expenses of the Observatory, on the condition of being furnished with daily reports.

The interest of the public was shown by their prompt response to the appeal made for subscriptions. A sum of over £4000 was soon collected, the subscriptions varying in amount from £200 to 1d.; and the List of Subscribers includes representatives of all ranks, from Her Majesty downwards.

The western side of Ben Nevis forms part of the estate of Callart, the property of Mrs. Cameron Campbell of Monzie, by whose kindness a feu of an acre was obtained on the top of the mountain for the Observatory, as well as the feu of a path thereto from the farm of Achintee, in Glen Nevis. On this site an Observatory, from plans by Mr. Sydney Mitchell, was erected. Telegraphic communication was established between the Observatory and Fort-William, so that the High-Level Observations might be compared with those made at the bottom, and the results sent out daily for the information of the public and to aid in the formation of weather forecasts.

Since for weeks at a time the Observatory on the top of the mountain is cut off from intercourse with Fort-William, and for months conveyance of provisions is practically impossible, the Observatory requires to be provisioned for nine months, while every other precaution that can be thought of is taken by the Directors to secure the safety and comfort of the observers.

To facilitate the access to the Observatory during the open season, a safe bridle-path, 6 feet wide, with gradients nowhere exceeding one in five, has been constructed by the Society from the farm of Achintee to the top of Ben Nevis. The route was suggested by Mr. Colin Livingston, and the construction of the road, as well as the Observatory buildings, was intrusted to Mr. James M'Lean, Fort-William. The original outlay on the road has been large, and, owing to the damage to bridges and exposed parts of the path by the floods of winter and spring, its annual maintenance is costly. Seeing that this road leads to the highest point of the British Islands, and commands along its course a series of the finest variegated views in Scotland, it is largely used by the public.

The Observatory on the summit was opened by Mrs. Cameron Campbell on 17th October 1883. Observations were begun in the following month, and have been carried on, as described in a previous chapter, ever since. At the same time a Sea-Level Station was opened at the Public School, Fort-William, under charge of Mr. C. Livingston, where comparison readings were taken five times a day with great punctuality and accuracy. But a few years showed the necessity of having a continuous record at sea-level as well as on the summit, and in 1889 the Directors resolved to carry out the original plan which want of funds had hitherto prevented, and set up a Low-Level Observatory. Aided by a grant from the Edinburgh Exhibition of 1886, and contributions from the public, they were able to erect a suitable building close to sea-level, on ground feued from Mr. Cameron of Lochiel, in the beginning of 1890. The Meteorological Council of London equipped this Station with self-recording instruments, and increased their annual grant to the Directors from £100 to £350. Observations began in the middle of July 1890, and since then there has been a continuous record of barometric pressure, temperature, humidity, rainfall, etc., by day and by night, both on the summit of Ben Nevis and at sea-level. The distance between the High- and Low-Level Observatories is only $4\frac{3}{4}$ miles, and their heights above sea-level respectively 4407 and 42 feet. Mr. Livingston also continued his observations for a year after the commencement of the Low-Level Observatory, so that there might be a satisfactory comparison of the two Sea-Level Stations. The telegraph wire from the summit has been extended to the Low-

Level Observatory, and the observers can communicate with each other at any time, and reports from both stations are sent daily to the newspapers. The High- and Low-Level Stations are worked as one Observatory, the observers being interchangeable, and the Low-Level serves also as a depôt for stores, etc., which are carried up during the summer to the top. The original build- ings on the hill-top consisted of one room 13 feet square, which had to serve as office, kitchen, telegraph- office, and general living-room, with three bedrooms opening off it, the other end of the oblong building being taken up with store-rooms, coal-cellar, etc. This was found too small for satisfactorily carrying on the work of the Observatory ; moreover, the doorway got blocked with snow, and exit was often impossible during storms, just when the observations of temperature and wind would have been most valuable. In the summer of 1884, large additions were therefore made, comprising another room to serve as laboratory and telegraph-office, two additional bedrooms, one of the old ones being converted into a pantry or store-room, a room to receive telegrams from visitors at times when it may be incon- venient to take strangers into the Observatory, and, most important, a tower about 30 feet high, which serves the double purpose of carrying a set of ane- mometers, and of providing a convenient exit when the winter snows have closed the ordinary doorway. The whole building is of a most substantial character. It is all on one story, except the tower, and consists of double wooden walls covered with felt, and surrounded by dry stone walls varying in thickness from 4 feet in the less exposed parts to 10 feet at the base of the tower; the windows are all double, and the roof is covered with lead, overlaid with snow boarding. The strength of the whole has been frequently tested by gales of a severity and duration never experienced at lower levels, and no damage has ever been received beyond the breaking of an occasional pane of glass by pieces of ice torn up and thrown against it by the wind. The only discomfort is in the first snows of winter; if the gutters get choked with hard ice, and a thaw comes, the water on the roof is ponded back and leaks in, but once the house is well covered with snow, the internal heat thaws them out again, and no further trouble is experienced. Even in spring and early summer, when the enormous masses of snow round are melting rapidly, the inside of the house is perfectly dry.

METEOROLOGY OF BEN NEVIS.

The chief points in the Meteorology of the Ben are succinctly given in the Table at page 64. The times are strictly the same for the two Observatories : *Ben Nevis* being the station on the summit of the mountain, and *Fort-William* that at the base.

Atmospheric Pressure.—The mean pressures at the two places are, in inches, for the year, 25·299 and 29·862 ; in January, when the minima occur, 25·185 and 29·793 ; and in June, the time of the maximum,

Fog crystals several feet thick.

Clearing away the drifted snows.

25·460 and 29·969. The annual mean monthly range is thus 0·275 at the top, and 0·176 at sea-level, the difference being due to temperature, as described below.

Temperature.—The lowest mean monthly temperature at Fort-William is 38°·7 in February, but on the top of Ben Nevis it is 22°·6 in March. The temperature of the Atlantic falls to the annual minimum in March, and it is in this month that the temperature of the air falls to the minimum at all Stations in the West of Scotland fully open to the influence of the Atlantic ; but in western situations not so exposed, such as Fort-William, temperature falls to the lowest point in February. It is interesting to note that the Ben Nevis Observatory, which is so high above all the mountains between it and the Atlantic, follows the Ocean as regards the time of occurrence of its annual minimum temperature. It is further of note that it is in March that the lowest maximum and also the lowest minimum temperatures have been recorded on the top of the Ben.

The horizontal distance between the two stations being only about four miles, the monthly variation in the difference of the atmospheric pressures at the two stations is virtually a temperature effect. As the temperature falls to the annual minimum in winter, the air contracts, and a portion of it consequently falls below the level of the barometer at the top, reducing the readings there, and thus increasing the differences between the two barometers. The difference then reaches 4·637 inches in March, the maximum difference for the year. On the other hand, as temperature rises, a portion of the atmosphere is raised above the level of the higher barometer, increasing the pressure there, and accordingly the difference is reduced to 4·486 inches in August, the minimum of the year. The difference between the maximum and minimum is thus 0·151 inch.

For these months the mean temperatures of the stratum of air between the top and bottom of the mountain are respectively 31°·0 and 47°·8, on the assumption that the mean temperature of the intervening air stratum is the mean of the temperatures at the top and bottom of the mountain. Hence the vertical displacement of the mass of the atmosphere for a temperature difference of 16°·8 is represented by a barometric difference of 0·151 inch. The sea-level pressures in these months are, however, respectively 29·863 in March and 29·828 inches in August. If, then, we assume the sea-level pressure of August to be the same as that of March, viz. 29·863 inches, the difference between the top and bottom pressures would be not 4·486, but 4·495 inches. From this it follows that the vertical displacement for a temperature difference of 16°·8, and at the same sea-level pressure, is 0·145 inch. In consideration of the successful arrangements which have been made to minimise the effects of solar and terrestrial radiation at both the High and the Low Level Observatories, and their close proximity to each other, the above result may be regarded as the most important datum hitherto contributed by Meteorology for the discussion of inquiries referring to the relations of height to pressure and temperature in the free atmosphere.

The highest mean monthly temperature at Fort-William is 56°·6, and at Ben Nevis Observatory 40°·0, both in July. A noteworthy feature of the temperature at the top is the comparatively small difference in the means of June, July, August, and September. At the top the temperature of September is only 0·8° lower than that of June; whereas at Fort-William the difference is 1°·6, the summer climate at the Observatory thus resembling that of all places in the West fully open to the Atlantic.

The highest mean temperature of any month, at the top, was 45°·6, in June 1887, in which month anti-cyclonic conditions ruled, with their usual accompaniment of dry warm weather; and the lowest mean temperature 20°·0, in January 1886, and again in March 1891. There was thus a difference of 25°·6. The absolutely highest temperature hitherto recorded at the top was 67°·0, on June 24th, 1887, and the lowest 2°·7, on March 27th, 1892, these being the readings from maximum and minimum thermometers. All the temperature entries in the table on page 64 are from the hourly readings at Ben Nevis and from self-recording instruments at Fort-William.

As regards the extreme temperatures for the months, it will be seen that the maxima at the two Observatories show very large differences in the summer, and small differences in the winter, months, the largest being 26°·6, in May, and the smallest 8°·1, in November. These striking differences are due in summer to the circumstance that the top is usually screened from the sun by mist and cloud at the times when very high temperatures occur below; and in winter the high temperatures at the top are due to the warmth of the anti-cyclone then prevailing, which high temperature is practically confined to the upper region of the mountain.

During these years the mean annual rainfall has been 142·34 inches, being the largest of any place in Scotland so far as known; and at Fort-William for the same period, 75·79 inches, or 66·55 inches more at the top than at the base of the mountain. If this excess increased in proportion to the height, it would be at the rate of 1½ per cent. per 100 feet of ascent. At the top the maximum amount is 17·22 inches, in January, and at Fort-William 10·37 inches, in the same month. The minimum amount is 5·53 inches at the top and 3·33 inches at Fort-William in April. The difference between the monthly amounts at the two places is greatest (8·29 inches) in September, and least (2·20 inches) in April. The differences, it will be remarked, increase steadily, increasing or diminishing from month to month, with the exception of March and November,—March showing an excess, and November a deficiency from the seasonal increase or decrease at these times of the year. From the peculiarity of the winds at those seasons, it is probable that these features of the rainfall are characteristic of the meteorology of the Ben. The exceptional case of September is wholly due to the unprecedentedly heavy fall in that month of 1891.

Meteorology of Ben Nevis

Generally over the north-west of Scotland, the rainfall shows a steady drop till May, and in the more northerly districts till June ; but on the top of the Ben the minimum clearly occurs in April, and by June the fall has already risen two inches above it. This is, perhaps, due to a more copious precipitation accompanying the ascending air-currents up the sides of the mountain during the warmer months, which may be regarded as commencing with May, when the temperature of the sides of the mountain begins to be higher than that of the surrounding atmosphere.

The figures, giving the percentage of each month's mean rainfall to that of the whole year, show that for the top the largest monthly rainfall, which occurs in January, is 11·6 per cent. of the annual amounts, whereas at Fort-William, the fall there is 13·5 per cent. ; and on the other hand, the rainfall at the top in April; the smallest month, is 3·9 per cent. of the annual fall, but at Fort-William the smallest monthly rainfall is 4·5 per cent. Thus at the top the rainfall has a larger monthly range. This peculiarity in the greater variability of the rainfall at the top of the mountain is very strongly brought out by the maximum and minimum falls of the individual months at the two Observatories. At the top the results give a mean monthly difference of 11·16 inches, whereas at Fort-William it is only 2·53, or nearly one-fifth of the difference at the top.

At the top the heaviest fall of any individual month was 43·55 inches, in September 1891 ; but at Fort-

Provisioning took place in summer.

William the rainiest month was January 1890, when 16·67 inches fell. The month of least rainfall was June 1891, when the amount at the top was only 1·94 inch, and at Fort-William only 0·84 inch.

At the Ben Nevis Observatory the number of fair days, or days on which less than one-hundredth of an inch of rain was measured, is 98. April stands first with 13 days, and June second with 12 days, and July lowest with 5 days. For individual months, the highest was August 1885 with 20 days; but in July 1886 and in January 1890 rain fell on every day of these months.

The annual average hours of sunshine is 733, the highest month being June, with 141 hours, and the lowest December, with 20 hours. In December the number has been persistently low, the highest even being only 28 hours in 1887. On the other hand, in June, the number was 250 hours in 1888, and exceeded 200 in 1887 and in 1889; whereas the highest number for any of the other eleven months was 162, in July 1885. This result is another expression of the fact that in the West Highlands June is the brightest and driest month of the year. The Table shows that the differences between the maximum and minimum numbers for the different years are very great; and the same remark holds good for the annual amounts of the different years.

As regards diurnal phenomena, the hourly variation for each month has been calculated for temperature, pressure, humidity, cloud, rainfall, wind velocity and direction, and sunshine. Results of the greatest importance in the development of Meteorology have been arrived at, for which, however, we must, in this brief sketch, refer the reader to the Observations, and Report thereon, published by the Royal Society of Edinburgh, as volume xxxiv. of their Transactions.

SPECIAL RESEARCHES AND DISCUSSIONS.

In addition to the usual work of a first-order meteorological observatory, other observations and researches have been carried on, mostly of a novel character, for which the Observatory affords exceptional facilities, and of which the following are the more prominent :—

Snow Crystals.—The formation in certain states of weather of *snow crystals*, from fog, on the Observatory and every object exposed to the drifting fogs, has been carefully observed and investigated by Mr. Omond. With these accretions, the cups of Robinson's anemometer are no longer hemispheres, but irregular hollow bodies, bristling all over with pointed crystals, and the arms increasing to many times their original thickness, the whole instrument soon becomes a mass of immovable snow-like crystals, and further observation is rendered impossible. The thermometer-box, with its louvre boards, similarly becomes serrated with rows of teeth, which quickly coalesce into a solid, so that the instruments are no longer in contact with the free atmosphere. In these circumstances a fresh box must be put out. It is thus that at observatories such as Ben Nevis, owing to these accretions of ice on the thermometers, the continuous or hourly registrations of the temperature of the air must be for ever impossible. Such observations must always be eye observations, where the observer personally sees, previously to the recording of each observation, that the thermometer is in contact with the free atmosphere, and is not sheltered from it by a coating of ice. The vital importance of thermometric observations is emphasised by the circumstance that without them the barometric observations are of comparatively small value, no approximation to a knowledge of the temperature of the air-stratum between the High and Low Level Observatories being possible. Ben Nevis is the only Observatory that has hitherto coped successfully with this all-important department of the work of a High-Level Observatory ; and one cannot sufficiently admire the heroic endurance with which the observers have made the hourly observations by night and by day, in all seasons, these years past.

Winds.—The winds, as regards direction, indicate a well-marked diurnal variation. From 3 to 8 a.m. northerly winds, blowing at the rate of two and a half miles per hour, and from 11 a.m. to 2 p.m. southerly winds, at three miles an hour, are most prevalent.

From a careful examination of the temperatures observed with the different winds, it has been shown that the mean temperatures are : S., 32°·6 ; S.W., 32°·5 ;

In a sea of snow.

Fog crystals built up on all exposed surfaces.

W., 31°·4 ; N.W. and S.E., 30°·2 ; E., 27°·8 ; N., 27°·6 ; and N.E., 26°·5. The warmest point in the thermic windrose oscillates from S.W. in winter, passing through S. to S.E. in summer. The annual temperature range of easterly winds is 20°·7, whereas in the case of westerly winds it is only 15°·6.

An exhaustive examination of the 'Winds of Ben Nevis,' by Messrs. Omond and Rankin, has been made, and the results published in the Transactions of the Royal Society of Edinburgh. It is shown that while the sea-level winds in this part of Scotland are, with respect to the distribution of pressure, in accordance with Buys Ballot's Law of the Winds, the Ben Nevis winds do not fit in with such a distribution of pressure, but, on the contrary, point to a widely different distribution of pressure at the height of the Observatory, 4407 feet above the sea, as compared with the distribution at sea-level. In large storms, with a deep barometric depression in the centre, the Ben Nevis winds are practically the same as at lower levels ; but with smaller storms, whose central depression is much less, great differences are presented. In such cases it is remarkable that with a cyclone covering Scotland, the North Sea, and Southern Norway, the winds frequently blow, not in accordance with the sea-level isobars, but in the opposite direction, suggesting an upper outflow from the cyclone towards the anti-cyclone adjoining it at the time. It is further remarkable that this outflowing seldom or never occurs when the centre of the storm is to the south or west, but only when it lies to the north or east, or in the region where, at the time, the weather is coldest and driest. If the wind on the hill-top is not at a right angle or a greater angle from the sea-level wind, it is usually nearly the same as it. The supposed veering of the wind at great heights, required by the theory that a cyclone is a whirling column, drawing the air in spirally below and pouring it out spirally above, is so seldom observed as to be the exception, and not the rule. This important result, and the analogous observation that frequently in great storms of winds prostrate trees lie practically in one direction over wide regions, show impressively how much observation has yet to contribute before a satisfactory theory or even a merely correct description of storms can be propounded.

The winds at Säntis, Puy de Dôme, and other High-Level European Observatories, which may all be practically regarded as situated in anti-cyclonic regions, have been examined, and it is found that they show the closest agreement with the winds at low levels in the same regions. This result separates the Ben Nevis Observatory from other Observatories, constituting it a class by itself, the differentiating cause being the circumstance that Ben Nevis alone lies in the central track of the European cyclones. This consideration emphasises the value of the Ben Nevis observations in all discussions of weather and atmospheric movements. It may be added that, with respect to the relation of the winds to the low-level isobars, Ben Nevis Observatory is more pronouncedly a High-Level Observatory in

winter than in summer, or, more generally, in cold than
in warm weather.

High Winds and Barometric Pressure.—In entering
on the examination and discussion of the hourly observations of the two Observatories, it soon became apparent that the influence of high winds on the barometer
was the first inquiry calling for serious attention. The
depression of the barometer during high winds was
plainly so great as to render the examination of many
questions all but a hopeless task until some approximation was made to the values of these depressions for
different wind velocities.

Fortunately the two Observatories present the
conditions favourable for this investigation. They are
so near to each other as to form virtually but one
Observatory, and while the barometer at the top is in
a building exposed to winds of all velocities up to at
least 150 miles an hour, the other barometer is in a
sheltered building and in a situation where light winds
prevail generally, but sufficiently open not to introduce
the errors that accompany readings in narrow valleys,
so that this barometer may be regarded as recording
the true pressure of the atmosphere. This was more
exactly secured, in making comparisons of the two
barometers, by selecting only those cases when winds
at the Fort-William Observatory were light. The
observations of the force of the wind are estima-
tions on a scale of 0 to 12, the equivalent of each
figure of the scale in miles per hour having been
carefully determined by Mr. Omond by means of a

Inside the half-way house.

Special Researches and Discussions

Robinson's anemometer. The barometric observations at the two Observatories were reduced to sea-level hour by hour, and the differences *plus* or *minus* were entered in columns representing the different wind forces at the higher Observatory. The following is the result of the comparison :

Wind Force	Eq. miles per hour	Bar. Depression Inch
0	2	— 0·001
1	7	— 0·004
2	13	— 0·005
3	21	— 0·010
4	29	— 0·014
5	38	— 0.026
6	47	— 0·035
7	57	— 0·050
8	67	— 0·070
9	77	— 0·104
10	88	— 0·122
11	99	— 0·150
11 to 12	111	— 0·170

Thus in calm weather the two reduced barometers are practically the same, but with every increase of wind which sweeps past the higher Observatory the depression of the barometer inside steadily augments. It is not till a velocity of more than 20 miles an hour is reached that the depression amounts to one-hundredth of an inch. At 57 miles it is 0·050 inch, at 77 miles 0·104 inch, and at 99 miles 0·150 inch. In forecasting weather it will be necessary to keep this effect of high winds on the barometer constantly in mind, with the view of arriving at a better approximation to the geographical distribution of pressure at the time the forecasts are being framed.

These results are for all winds taken together irrespective of their direction. The next inquiry grouped the winds according to their direction to sixteen points of the compass. During the time under examination, all the very high winds were from E.S.E. or S.E., these being the directions in which the wind blows most freely towards the Observatory. In eleven cases the wind from these directions attained a velocity of 100 miles an hour or more, and the reduced barometer of the high-level station read about one-sixth of an inch lower than the barometer of the Low-Level Observatory. In no other of the sixteen directions was there, during the ten months, a higher velocity than 60 miles an hour observed; and indeed in the directions E., E.N.E., N.E., N., N.W., and W. the observed velocity has been at no time greater than 30 miles an hour. With these winds the observations at the top of the mountain indicate a much lower speed than that which, from the drift of the lower clouds, is seen to be reached at a comparatively small height above the top of the Ben. The cause of this comparatively calm state of the air immediately on the top is the impact of the air on the face of the tremendous cliff, nearly 1800 feet high, close to the edge of which the Observatory is built, by which the stream lines are suddenly deflected upwards. Now, in such cases, the depression of the barometer is about three times as great as that which occurs with an equally strong wind from other directions, and indicates clearly the formation of a restricted region of low pressure around and outside the Observatory. This essential difference between winds from E. by N. to W. which strike the precipices from the winds blowing from the other points of the compass must be steadily kept in view in all discussions of the weather ; and it must be added that further investigation is required to a right understanding of them. Another curious and highly interesting result observed with other directions of the wind is that the reduced high-level barometer exceeds the reduced low-level barometer when the wind blows at the rate of about 5 miles an hour. This increased pressure accompanying wind rising up the slope of the hill may perhaps explain the small clear space immediately on the top of a hill, otherwise cloud-topped, and the very different force of wind on the two sides of a ridge lying at about right angles to the direction of the wind.

Relation of Differences of Temperature to those of Pressure.—An examination has also been made of the relations of differences of temperature at the two Observatories to differences of the sea-level pressures at the same hours. During the ten months examined, the temperature differences have ranged from the High-Level Observatory showing a temperature 26° lower to a temperature 6° higher than the temperature at Fort-William at the time. A comparison has been made by sorting the differences into two-degrees amounts, and instituting a comparison only on those cases when the strength of the wind at either of the Observatories did not exceed 26 miles an hour.

The following show for each two-degrees difference

of temperature the difference between the reduced barometer at the top and the barometer at Fort-William, the *plus* sign indicating that the top barometer was the higher, and the *minus* sign that it was the lower of the two :—

Difference of Temperature	Difference of Pressure Inch	Difference of Temperature	Difference of Pressure Inch
+6° to +4°	+0·047	−10° to −12°	+0·006
+4 ,, +2	+0·044	−12 ,, −14	+0·001
+2 ,, +0	+0·041	−14 ,, −16	−0·005
−0 ,, −2	+0·031	−16 ,, −18	−0·010
−2 ,, −4	+0·020	−18 ,, −20	−0·017
−4 ,, −6	+0·009	−20 ,, −22	−0·023
−6 ,, −8	+0·011	−22 ,, −24	−0·026
−8 ,, −10	+0·009	−24 ,, −26	−0·029

Hence during the period of occurrence of the anti-cyclone, when the temperature at the top of the mountain, with reference to that at Fort-William, is highest, the pressure at the top, reduced to sea-level, is 0·047 inch higher than at Fort-William ; and, on the other hand, when the temperature at the top is very greatly lower than the average as compared with that at Fort-William, the pressure at the top, reduced to sea-level, is 0·029 inch lower than that at Fort-William. There is, therefore, a mean difference of 0·076 inch of pressure for these two distinct types of weather. The broad result is this, and it is clear and explicit, that when the higher Observatory has the higher temperature, and also when the differences of temperature are small, then the reduced pressure at the top of the mountain is the greater of the two ; but when the differences of temperature are large, then the reduced pressure at the top is the lesser of the two. The all but regular progression of these figures shows that what is substantially a true average has been obtained. The result, which is altogether unexpected, raises questions of the greatest importance, affecting the theory of storms, the effect of vertical movements of great masses of air on the barometric pressure which accompanies cyclones and anticyclones, and the necessity there is for some accurate knowledge of the absolute amounts of aqueous vapour at different heights in the atmosphere under different weather conditions, and how this knowledge may be arrived at from the readings of the dry and wet bulb thermometers under different atmospheric pressures. Ben Nevis, with its two Observatories, one at the top, the other at the foot of the mountain, would, with a third halfway up the hill, afford unique facilities for the prosecution of this all-important hygrometric inquiry, which would, however, require considerable additions, for the time it is carried on, to the Observatories' present appliances and staff.

Rainband.—Observations of the rainband were begun in June 1885, from which the following results have been obtained:—The observed higher values are accompanied, or soon followed, by a heavy rainfall, which tends, however, to become less heavy in the next twelve hours. The lowest values, on the other hand, though they may be neither accompanied nor followed in the next three hours by any rain, are followed by a considerable rainfall before the twelve hours are run, thus indicating that an unusually dry atmosphere, as revealed

Observatory Hotel, once Britain's highest hostelry.

Ready for the off on an early Ben race.

by the spectroscope, is frequently the precursor of heavy rains. With the same rainband value precipitation is less with a higher and greater with a lower temperature. If the temperature immediately falls, the rainfall is greatly increased, but if it rises, it is less than it would have been if the temperature remained constant. The highest values, with accompanying very heavy rains, are part and parcel of the cyclones which come to us from the Atlantic laden with moisture and warmth. The rainband is not affected during those heavy rains which are the result of moisture-laden air ascending the mountain from lower levels; and during those states of the air which attend the rapid deposition of snow crystals no rain or snow falls, though at the time the rainband values are high.

As respects forecasting the weather, the most important observations are those which indicate a decreasing rainband from hour to hour. A comparison of these observations with the Daily Weather-Charts and subsequent observations, show that the decreasing rainband indicates that the moist air aloft is slipping away or sinking below the level of the summit, and that the air taking its place is comparatively dry. Now this state of things appears to be the earliest indication we at present have that an anti-cyclone is beginning to form and settle over North-Western Europe.

St. Elmo's Fire.—Cases of St. Elmo's Fire are not infrequent occurrences on Ben Nevis. The cases observed have mostly occurred during the night, and during the winter months from September to February. A

careful discussion of these cases shows that the weather
which precedes, accompanies, and follows has quite
peculiar characteristics not only on Ben Nevis but also
over the West of Europe generally; indeed, so well
marked is the type of weather, and so notorious is it for
its stormy character, that it is familiarly known at the
Observatory as 'St. Elmo's weather.' It is further
observed that in almost every case another cyclone,
with its spell of bad weather, follows the particular
cyclone on the south-eastern side of which St. Elmo's
Fire is observed.

Thunderstorms.—The winter thunderstorms are observed under the identical weather conditions under
which St. Elmo's Fire occurs; that is, they invariably
occur on the south-east side of the cyclone's centre,
with the easterly passage of which they appear to be
intimately connected. The thunderstorms and cases
of sheet-lightning of Ben Nevis are essentially autumn
and winter occurrences, 70 per cent. of the whole having occurred from September to February. They are
rare in summer, only eight having occurred from May
to August, and thus have an annual period the re-
verse of what obtains in the eastern districts of Scotland. During the summer they are twice as frequent
at Fort-William as at the Observatory, thus suggesting
that a considerable number must be wholly below the
summit, or in the aerial stratum between the High and
Low Level Observatories. All the summer thunderstorms
have occurred when the sun was above the horizon;
but of the thirty-seven cases in autumn and winter

thirty-two took place when the sun was below the horizon. These results are of no small value in relation to the distribution of thunderstorms and other electrical displays over the land and the water surfaces of the globe.

Silver Thaw.—The phenomena of Silver Thaw, or rain falling when the air is below freezing-point, and congealing as it falls, have been discussed by Mr. R. C. Mossman. The phenomenon points to an inversion of temperature at the time, so that the temperature on the top of the Ben is considerably lower than at higher altitudes. From 1885 to 1890 there occurred 198 cases, lasting in all 873 hours—that is, cases in which rain froze as it fell. The maximum frequency is from November to March ; indeed, nearly all the cases have occurred in these months. It occasions, as may well be supposed, much inconvenience and discomfort to the observers. The chief point that has been established is that the distribution of pressure over Western Europe is at the time always substantially the same. The Daily Weather-Charts show that on these 198 days the distribution of pressure was for the Ben cyclonic on 137 and anti-cyclonic on 61 days. In anti-cyclonic cases a cyclone is off the north-west coast of Norway, while the anti-cyclone stretches away over the south of England and Ireland. In cyclonic cases Ben Nevis is clearly within the area of low pressure, the centre of which again is off the north-west coast of Norway, while the anti-cyclone is removed farther to the southward over the peninsula. Hence the value of this phenomenon in forecasting

Drifting around the windows and doors.

weather. The average duration is 6 hours in winter and 3 in summer. The longest continued was 41 hours, on January 3-4, 1889. The lowest temperature at which it has occurred was 18°, but nearly in all cases the occurrence takes place shortly before a thaw, or slightly under 32°. In cyclonic cases of silver thaw, temperature begins to rise 15 hours before the phenomenon commences, and continues rising during the occurrence, then falls, until the sixth hour after it has ceased, after which it again rises. The barometer falls steadily till the phenomenon sets in, rises during the fall and until five hours after it has ceased, when it again begins to fall, this fall coinciding with a distinct backing of the wind and rise of temperature, thus indicating clearly that another cyclone is fast advancing on North-Western Europe. In anti-cyclonic cases, temperature rises for 18 hours before and continues rising till three hours after the phenomenon, and then steadily falls. The barometer rises till the fall of the silver thaw commences, and thereafter continues falling steadily during and after the phenomenon. It is a noteworthy circumstance that with silver thaw temperature rises more rapidly in cyclonic than in anti-cyclonic cases, the rate in cyclonic cases being more than double that in anti-cyclonic cases.

At the Ben Nevis Observatory, silver thaws are seldom associated with strong winds, but at low levels they are immediately preceded and followed by frequent gales on the northern and north-western coasts of Scotland, thus furnishing another illustration of one of the most important conclusions established by the Ben Nevis observations that the barometric gradient at the height of Ben Nevis (4407 feet) is often totally different from this gradient at sea-level during the time of occurrence of silver thaw at the top. The commencement of silver thaw preceded the commencement of gales on these British coasts in 75 per cent. of the cases. If silver thaw occurs on Ben Nevis, when an anti-cyclone lies over England, and a barometric depression is lying off the west of Norway, the tendency of the weather over the British Isles is to become steadily worse.

Hygrometric Observations.—An elaborate series of hygrometric observations has been made at the Observatory with the view of inquiring how far Glaisher's factors can be used in order to arrive at results satisfactorily approximate to the truth. For the conduct of such an inquiry, the low-temperature humidities and remarkably dry states of the atmosphere which form so prominent a feature in the climatology of Ben Nevis, the Observatory offers unique facilities. The first series of special observations was made by Mr. H. N. Dickson, with the ordinary dry and wet bulb hygrometer and Professor Chrystal's direct hygrometer, with the result that a specially constructed set of tables is required for the extremely low humidities of Ben Nevis, these being considerably lower than Mr. Glaisher had had an opportunity of observing. Mr. A. J. Herbertson has more recently commenced an examination of the hygrometry of the atmosphere by direct measurement of the quantities of aqueous vapour present, and comparison with the dry and wet bulb readings at the same time and place. It is expected from these experiments that the variation in the hygrometry of the atmosphere at different heights under varying conditions of weather will be ascertained. As already indicated, an examination of the utility of the dry and wet bulb hygrometer in arriving at a correct knowledge of the absolute and relative humidities is urgently required, for conducting which the ranges of pressures, temperatures, and humidities afforded by the two Observatories give the indispensable conditions for the data of observations.

Electric Currents.—Professor C. Michie Smith has shown that on the edge of a dissolving mist the potential is lower than the normal, but higher on the edge of a condensing mist. Now, almost always when the top of Ben Nevis becomes clear for a short time, a strong current comes up the telegraph cable, while as soon as the summit is again enveloped the current is reversed. The connection between the moisture of the atmosphere and the earth currents is still further shown by the rainfall. During a fall of rain or snow the current nearly always passes down the cable ; and in the case of a sudden shower the current has sometimes driven the mirror of the galvanometer violently off the scale. A cessation of the rain or snow generally has an exactly opposite effect. If it be assumed that the summit of Ben Nevis takes the potential of the masses of vapour covering it, and if we consider the earth-plate at the

Collecting melted snow.

Half way house, with lochan in the background.

base as the earth, or zero of potential, it is obvious that the results confirm the theory advanced by Professor Michie Smith, a conclusive proof of which would be of the greatest importance in investigations connected with thunderstorms.

Dust Particles in the Atmosphere.—This important branch of meteorological inquiry was originated by Mr. John Aitken in 1889. By means of Aitken's dust-counting apparatus the numbers of dust particles per cubic centimètre of air can be ascertained with great exactness. After some preliminary observations and inquiries, observations of the ·dust of the atmosphere became part of the regular work of the Observatory ; the observations being made eight times daily at intervals of three hours. For the three months ending May 1891 the following are the mean numbers per cubic centimètre for each of the hours of observation :—

	A.M.				P.M.				
	1	4	7	11	1	4	7	11	Day
Mean Numbers,	736	526	570	551	950	1438	1035	1029	854
Difference from Mean, . .	-118	-328	-284	-303	+96	+584	+181	+175	..

These results indicate a well-defined diurnal period. The forenoon values are all under, and the afternoon values above the daily mean. The minimum, 526, occurs at 4 a.m., and the maximum, 1438, at 4 p.m., the latter being from two to three times greater than the former. The maximum occurs at the time of the afternoon minimum barometer, when the ascending aerial current from lower levels is at the daily maximum. The increased impurity of the air, as measured by the numbers of dust particles observed, is due to these ascending air-currents. On the other hand, the minimum occurs at the time of the morning minimum barometer, when the effects of terrestrial radiation reach the daily maximum, and, at the same time, the wind at the top rises to its daily maximum, thus indicating in no obscure manner that at this time the air-currents have descended from higher levels. Hence, while the maximum numbers occur when the ascending current is strongest, the minimum numbers occur when the descending current is most pronounced. This is an important contribution to our knowledge of the diurnal movements of the atmosphere.

From the whole of the observations on Ben Nevis, the mean is 696 per cubic centimètre, the maximum being 14,400, while on several occasions the minimum fell to 0. In a large number of observations made by Mr. Aitken at Kingairloch, on the west shore of Loch Linnhe, the average number was 1600 particles per cubic centimetre; in London he found, on one occasion, 100,000, and this number was exceeded in Paris.

Dry thick fog, as a rule, contains a great amount of dust, but thin wet mist very little. Indeed, it is when a thin drizzling mist envelops the summit that the lowest values are always obtained; and the all-important observation is noted that at that time the winds at the summit differ in direction by 90° or more from the winds at Fort-William. At such times it is evident that the drizzling and practically dustless winds at the summit blow out from a shallow cyclone overspreading that part of Europe at the time. The vital importance to weather forecasting of the relations of these different types of wind, either as dustless or dusty, to the cyclones and anti-cyclones at the time is seen at once.

A sea of rolling mist fills the valleys.

The low-level observatory in Fort William.